Journey to English

CARLA MAURÍCIO C. DA S. VIANNA
MARIANNA VEIGA TAVARES

2

WORKBOOK

© Carla Maurício C. da S. Vianna e Marianna Veiga Tavares, 2013

Diretora editorial: Ana Claudia Ferrari
Gerente editorial: Gisele Aga
Editora de arte: Simone Oliveira Vieira
Designer: Ivan Toledo Prado
Assistente de arte: Carol Duran
Pesquisadora iconográfica: Gabriela Farcetta
Coordenadora de produto: Carla Rodrigues Riquena
Assistente de redação: Elena Regina Pucinelli
Coordenadora de produção gráfica: Roseli Said

Editora de conteúdo: Luciana Macias Pimentel
Editores-assistentes: Fernando Santos, Silene Cardoso
Preparadora: Sâmia Rios
Revisor linguístico: Robert Caudler Garner
Projeto gráfico: Ivan Toledo Prado
Edição de arte e diagramação: Estúdio Sintonia
Capa: Ivan Toledo Prado
Ilustrações: Giz de Cera Studio (Sidney Meireles)
Iconografia: Etoile Shaw, Gabriela Farcetta, Odete Ernestina Pereira
Tratamento de imagens: Paulo César Salgado

Créditos das fotos:
p. 3: © Prudkov/Dreamstime.com; p. 4: © iStockPhoto/Thinkstock; © Calvin & Hobbes, Bill Watterson © 1990 Watterson / Dist. by Universal Uclick; p. 6: © Anthony Pappone/Flickr Vision/Getty Images; p. 8: © Nalukai/Dreamstime.com; © iStockphoto/Thinkstock; © iStockphoto/Thinkstock; © ImageSource/Macmillan Image Bank; © Andres Rodriguez/Dreamstime.com; © Vadim Kulikov/Dreamstime.com; p. 9: © Lisa Payne/Macmillan Education; © Sf1nks/Dreamstime.com; © Matt Antonino/Dreamstime.com; © Norberto Mario Lauría/Dreamstime.com; © Benbro/Dreamstime.com; © Margouillat/Dreamstime.com; © iStockphoto/Thinkstock; © iStockphoto/Thinkstock; © Grafvision/Dreamstime.com; © iStockphoto/Thinkstock; © Jacek Chabraszewski/Dreamstime.com; p. 10: © Monkey Business Images/Dreamstime.com; © iStockphoto/Thinkstock; © Banana Stock/Thinkstock; © Dzmitri Mikhaltsov/Dreamstime.com; p. 15: © iStockphoto/Thinkstock; © Annatamila/Dreamstime.com; © Vanessagifford/Dreamstime.com; © Valua Vitaly/Dreamstime.com; © Bfphoto/Dreamstime.com; © Kmiragaya/Dreamstime.com; p. 18: © Viorel Sima/Dreamstime.com; © Zurijeta/Dreamstime.com; © Daniel Cymbalista/Pulsar Imagens; © Juan Moyano/Dreamstime.com; © Adamgregor/Dreamstime.com; © Valua Vitaly/Dreamstime.com; p. 22: © Mirco Vacca/Dreamstime.com; © iStockphoto/Thinkstock; © Dmitry Kalinovsky/Dreamstime.com; © B2M Productions/Photographer's Choice/Getty Images; © Adamgregor/Dreamstime.com; © Hongqi Zhang/Dreamstime.com; p. 23: © Ron Chapple/Dreamstime.com; © Rozenn Leard/Dreamstime.com; © Spotmatik/Dreamstime.com; © Sang Lei/Dreamstime.com; © Photowitch/Dreamstime.com; © Wavebreak Media/Thinkstock; p. 27: © Fuse/Thinkstock; © Comstock/Thinkstock; p. 28: © Comstock/Thinkstock; p. 30: © Banana Stock/Thinkstock; p. 31: © iStockphoto/Thinkstock; p. 32: © Cyanide and Happiness © Explosm.net

Todos os esforços foram feitos no sentido de encontrar os detentores dos direitos das obras protegidas por *copyright*. Caso tenha havido alguma omissão involuntária, a editora terá o maior prazer em corrigi-la na primeira oportunidade.

```
Dados Internacionais de Catalogação na Publicação (CIP)
       (Câmara Brasileira do Livro, SP, Brasil)

       Vianna, Carla Maurício C. da S.
          Journey to English Workbook / Carla Maurício C.
       da S. Vianna, Marianna Veiga Tavares. -- 1. ed. --
       Cotia, SP : Macmillan, 2013.

          Obra em 4 v.
          ISBN 978-85-7418-880-5 (Journey to english 1 )
          ISBN 978-85-7418-937-6 (Journey to english 2 )
          ISBN 978-85-7418-938-3 (Journey to english 3 )
          ISBN 978-85-7418-939-0 (Journey to english 4 )

          1. Inglês (Ensino fundamental) I. Tavares,
       Marianna Veiga. II. Título.

13-04091                                    CDD-372.652

               Índices para catálogo sistemático:

       1. Inglês : Ensino fundamental    372.652
```

Reprodução proibida. Art. 184 do Código Penal e Lei 9.610 de 19 de fevereiro de 1998.
Todos os direitos reservados.

MACMILLAN DO BRASIL
Rua José Félix de Oliveira, 383 – Granja Viana
Cotia – SP – 06708-645
www.macmillan.com.br
Atendimento ao professor: (11) 4613-2278
0800 16 88 77 (Outras regiões)
Fax: (11) 4612-6098

Impresso no Brasil - Gráfica Ave Maria - Janeiro/2015

UNIT 1 — *A day in the life*

1 **Complete the dialog with the words from the box.**

> boarder • boarding school • grade • Saturdays
> schedule • students • weekdays

Pedro: Hi, Marcos!

Marcos: Hi, Pedro! How are you? You're in a new school, aren't you?

Pedro: Yeah, I'm a .... now!

Marcos: Really? Where is your ....?

Pedro: It's in California.

Marcos: Cool! Do you like it? Do you study on .... as well?

Pedro: I really like it. I don't study on Saturdays, only on ....

Marcos: Are you in .... 7 there?

Pedro: Yes, I am. There are thirty-two .... in my class.

Marcos: What about your school ....?

Pedro: Well, some subjects are different now. Marcos, I have to go.

Marcos: OK! Good to see you!

2 **Circle the correct times.**

a `3:45` – three forty-five / fifteen to three

b `12:00` a.m. – midday / midnight

c `9:05` – five to nine / nine oh five

d `6:50` – ten to seven / six fifteen

3 **Match the columns. Then fill in the blanks with the correct verbs.**

a take

b arrive

c do

d play

e go

f use

○ I don't .... my homework after dinner.

○ I prefer to .... a shower before breakfast.

○ I .... the Internet in the afternoon.

○ We don't .... soccer at school.

○ I .... to bed before 10:00 p.m.

○ I .... home at 1:00 p.m. on weekdays.

4 Unscramble the words and complete the sentences.

Hi, my name is Carlos and this is my weekly routine.

I .... (akwe) up every day at 6:30 a.m. Then I take a .... (orhswe) and have .... (rfbtksaea) with my family. On Mondays and Wednesdays I go to .... (ocsloh) with my dad, by car. On the other days I .... (aklw) to school with my friends Paulo and Camila. Our .... (lsasesc) start at 7:30 a.m. and .... (ihifns) at 12:00 p.m. I don't have lunch at school; I have lunch at home, at 1:00 p.m. Between 2:00 p.m. and 4:00 p.m. I do my .... (ohowekmr). Then, it's time to have fun: video games, skating, biking – and on Thursdays and Fridays, I play .... (lollebvlya) at a local gym. Dinner is served at about 7:00 p.m. After dinner I .... (ahwtc) TV or read a book (I'm really into reading!) and go to .... (dbe) at 10:00 p.m. Except on Fridays, when it's party time!

5 Read the Calvin comic strip and write T (true) or F (false).

a Calvin is happy with his daily routine.

b He does something very unusual.

c Calvin's father is very calm and happy.

d In the end, Calvin doesn't change his routine.

4

6 Write sentences in the affirmative (+) or negative (x) forms.

a We / have breakfast / 9:30 a.m. (x)

....

b I / do my homework / in the evening. (x)

....

c My parents / go to bed / 11:00 p.m. (+)

....

d They / watch TV / after 10:00 p.m. (x)

....

e My brother and I / play computer games / Saturdays. (+)

....

7 Now, write six sentences about your daily activities. Use *do* and *don't*. Follow the examples.

I wake up at 6:30 a.m.
I don't go to school by car.

My routine

....

....

....

....

....

....

....

....

....

....

....

....

UNIT 2 — The haves and havenots

1 Read the text about an African festival and underline the verbs in the third person singular.

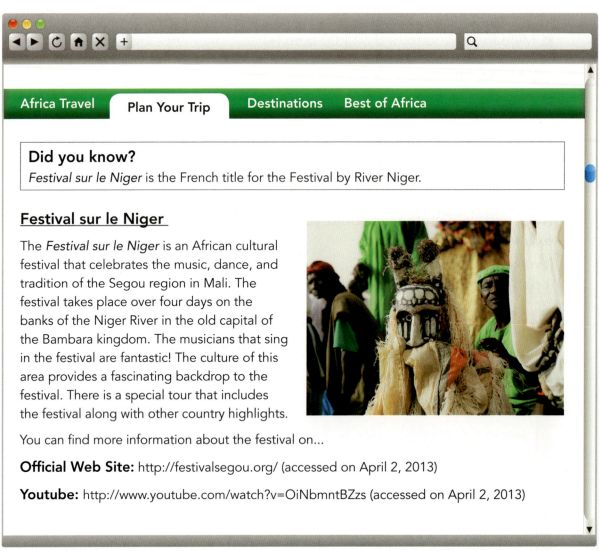

Africa Travel | Plan Your Trip | Destinations | Best of Africa

Did you know?
Festival sur le Niger is the French title for the Festival by River Niger.

Festival sur le Niger

The *Festival sur le Niger* is an African cultural festival that celebrates the music, dance, and tradition of the Segou region in Mali. The festival takes place over four days on the banks of the Niger River in the old capital of the Bambara kingdom. The musicians that sing in the festival are fantastic! The culture of this area provides a fascinating backdrop to the festival. There is a special tour that includes the festival along with other country highlights.

You can find more information about the festival on...

Official Web Site: http://festivalsegou.org/ (accessed on April 2, 2013)

Youtube: http://www.youtube.com/watch?v=OiNbmntBZzs (accessed on April 2, 2013)

Adapted from <http://goafrica.about.com>. Accessed on April 2, 2013. © 2013 Anouk Zijlma (http://goafrica.about.com). Used with permission of About Inc., which can be found online at www.about.com. All rights reserved.

2 Read the text "Festival sur le Niger" again and check the correct alternatives.

- ○ The text mentions different material possessions.
- ○ The festival is a life experience.
- ○ There are no tours that include the festival.
- ○ It's a festival that celebrates the traditions of the Segou region.
- ○ The festival takes place on the banks of the Nile River.

3 **Match the columns to form sentences.**

a Richard does ⟶ ◯ to London every year.

b Patty uses ◯ a new digital music player.

c Maria travels ◯ his homework in the afternoon.

d Peter buys ◯ the Internet on weekdays.

e Waleska has ◯ brand-name clothes.

4 **Complete the sentences with the correct form of the verbs in parentheses.**

a Thiago .... to school by bus every day. (go – affirmative)

b Linda .... hard. She .... bad grades on her
report card. (study – negative / have – affirmative)

c My brother .... at an international company. (work – affirmative)

d Jill .... in the office this week. She .... a lot on
business. (be – negative / travel – affirmative)

e Claire .... TV all day long. She .... such a couch
potato! (watch – affirmative / be – affirmative)

f Albert is late again. It .... all the time! (happen – affirmative)

5 **Find and circle the mistakes. Then rewrite the sentences correctly.**

a Nassin study at an American school.

....

b The NGO donate clothes to homeless people.

....

c Cecilia watchs TV every night.

....

d My dad not like Spanish food.

....

e I think my dog is sick. It don't want to drink water.

....

7

6 Put the words in the correct order and write the sentences under the corresponding photos. Then write LE for life experience or MP for material possession.

a buy / wants / new / my / car / father / to / a / .

b year / my / visit / wants / to / next / France / mother / .

c wants / brother / an / in / elephant / my / ride / India / to / .

d her / wants / my / vacation / Hawaii / on / sister / to / in / surf / .

e hot air balloon / next / aunt / to / fly / wants / Turkey / in / summer / my / a / in / .

f uncle / to / my / a / buy / house / wants / big / .

7 Now it's your turn. Write two sentences about your future expectations.

I want to...
Life experience: ....
Material possession: ....

UNIT 3 Breakfast of champions

1 Find ten breakfast items in the word search. Then write the words next to the photos.

```
N P D O C H E E S E P H N R
S Y O R A N G E J U I C E A
F O P T K R D E C F S N N U
R T D R E I A S T G I F T S
U B B A T E P N E H E D N U
I C B N D N P F U N S T O T
T C A T S D L C O S T U M E
R B O K E S E R P O C I H I
E U R O E V T I E S E D A D
A R D E F E P F J X R B M R
I N V I A A T I O N E A R D
A M Y T R D W B A N A N A F
I H A T C I M R V O L N I T
```

 A glass of ....

 An ....

 A slice of ....

 A ....

A piece of ....

A bowl of ....

A slice of ....

A bowl of ....

A cup of ....

A slice of ....

2 Answer the question about you.

What do you have for breakfast?

....

9

3 Match the photos to the sentences.

a

b

c

d

○ I don't drink milk.
I'm allergic to it.

○ I drink orange juice every day.

○ I'm thirsty. I need a glass of water.

○ Do you like chocolate cake?

4 Check *Do* or *Does*. Then complete the questions.

a .... Emily like ham?

○ Do   ○ Does

b .... you eat Japanese food?

○ Do   ○ Does

c .... your brother prepare his own breakfast?

○ Do   ○ Does

d .... we have to go to school on foot today?

○ Do   ○ Does

5 Complete the questions with *do* or *does* and write the correct
answers. Pay attention to the cues in parentheses.

> + = yes
>
> x = no

a .... your uncle drink a cup of coffee after dinner? (+)

....

b .... your father eat toast and eggs for breakfast? (x)

....

c .... your friends order pizza on Wednesdays? (x)

....

d .... your sister cook pasta for lunch? (+)

....

6 Make questions for these answers.

a ....

Yes, she does. Agnes drinks a cup of tea every day.

b ....

No, I don't. I don't eat meat because I'm a vegetarian.

c ....

Yes, she does. Laura makes a delicious orange cake.

d ....

No, it doesn't. Carol's cat doesn't drink milk because it's allergic to it.

7 Unscramble the words to form questions. Then give your answers to them.

a prepare / does / for / father / breakfast / you / your / ?

....

....

....

b have / does / mother / your / in the morning / cereal / ?

....

....

....

c you / like / do / Japanese / food / ?

....

....

....

d your / friend / juice / best / does / orange / drink / ?

....

....

....

e your / eat / do / for / fruit / parents / breakfast / ?

....

....

....

UNIT 4 — What's that smell?

1 Complete the clues below. Then use these words to solve the crossword.

DOWN
1. I have to clip my ....
2. Don't pick your .... It's disgusting!

ACROSS
3. Go wash your .... Your makeup is a mess.
4. Your .... looks funny. You have to comb it.
5. Wash your .... It's lunchtime.
6. Don't forget to brush your .... before you go to bed.

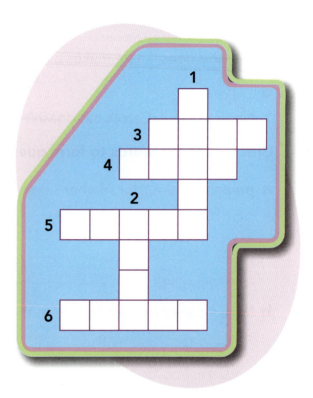

2 Rewrite the sentences. Use the adverbs of frequency from the box.

always • often • rarely • sometimes

a Mark uses foot powder four times a week.

....

b Ronald bites his nails all the time.

....

c Sarah washes her hair twice a week.

....

d Phil uses dental floss once a week.

....

3 Write your answers in the correct boxes.

always

....
....
....
....

often

....
....
....
....

How often do you ...
floss?
go to the dentist?
take a shower?
clean your shoes?
have a haircut?
comb your hair?
brush your teeth?
use foot powder?

sometimes

....
....
....
....

rarely

....
....
....
....

4 Classify the following hygiene expressions. Write BH for bad habits and GH for good habits.

○ take a shower

○ wear dirty socks

○ use foot powder

○ comb your hair

○ wear stinky sneakers

○ clip your nails

○ pick your nose

○ wash your hands

5 Interview a classmate about his/her habits. Then write the answers. Use adverbs and expressions of frequency.

   a How often does your classmate wash his/her hair?
   ....

   b How often does he/she eat fruit?
   ....

   c How often does he/she drink water?
   ....

   d How often does he/she use mouthwash?
   ....

   e How often does he/she bite his/her nails?
   ....

6 Fill in the blanks and find out some disgusting habits. Use the clues in parentheses.

a She is always smelly. She only .... once a week. (shower)

b Peter rarely changes his clothes. He often .... clothes. (dirty)

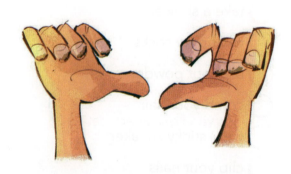

c My brother's feet don't smell good. He never .... (foot powder)

d Flávio's nails are often long. He rarely .... (nails)

14

UNIT 5

Yes, we can!

1 Observe the subject pronouns in *italics*. Then choose the right possessive adjectives to complete the sentences.

a *We* can't read without .... glasses.
- ( ) our
- ( ) its

b Anita can't drive .... car because *she* has a broken leg.
- ( ) her
- ( ) his

c Girls, when can *you* practice .... dance moves?
- ( ) her
- ( ) your

d .... name is William. *He's* a taxi driver.
- ( ) Her
- ( ) His

e *I* can play chess but .... parents can't.
- ( ) my
- ( ) their

2 Use the possessive adjectives in the box to fill in the blanks. Pay attention to the words in bold. Then match the sentences to the photos.

> her • his • my • our • their • your

a Look at **Paul and Betty!** .... books are very heavy.

b Who do **you** meet on .... weekends?

c Does **Ann** like .... mom's sweets?

d **I** don't have free time during the week because I have to do .... homework.

e **We** love physical education. At .... school, we have two P.E. classes a week.

f **Anthony** has a bike. .... bike is new.

15

3 **Read the dialogs. Then underline the best options.**

a **A:** Hello, **my** / **its** name's Andrea. What's **my** / **your** name?
B: My name is Alex and this is **my** / **his** brother. **His** / **Her** name is Thomas.

b **A:** Guys, our teachers can't hand out **its** / **our** tests before December.
B: Really? Why?
A: Because **her** / **their** coordinator is on vacation and won't be back till then.

c **A:** That woman over there is **my** / **his** aunt.
B: Is she **her** / **your** mother's sister?
A: No, she's **my** / **your** father's sister. She's American and **her** / **our** name is Pamela.
B: Let's go say *hi*.

4 **Complete the sentences using can (✓) or can't (✗) and the appropriate possessive adjective.**

a Jennifer .... (✓) do a lot of body tricks with .... tongue.

b I .... (✗) wink with .... left eye.

c My friends and I .... (✓) touch .... noses with .... tongues.

d Dad .... (✓) reduce stress by squeezing .... stress ball.

e This old cell phone .... (✗) detect wi-fi connections anymore, but .... cell phone can.

f Awesome! You .... (✓) roll back .... eyes!

16

5 **Use the information in the table to decide if the sentences are True (T) or False (F). Then correct the wrong information.**

	Howard	Dennis	Sylvia	Ted	Gary	Helen	Mary
speak English	x	✓	✓	x	✓	✓	x
sing	x	✓	x	✓	x	x	✓
whistle	✓	x	✓	x	✓	x	✓
jump rope	✓	x	✓	✓	x	✓	✓
stand on one leg	x	✓	x	x	✓	x	✓
play the piano	x	✓	✓	✓	x	x	x
surf	✓	x	✓	x	✓	✓	x
write poems	x	x	x	✓	✓	✓	✓

a Gary can speak English and whistle, but he can't sing or jump rope. ◯

....

b Howard, Sylvia, Gary, and Helen can't stand on one leg. ◯

....

c Dennis can speak English, sing, stand on one leg, and surf. ◯

....

d Mary can write poems, but she can't speak English. ◯

....

e Ted can't surf, but he can jump rope. ◯

....

f Howard, Helen, and Mary can't play the piano, but they can write poems. ◯

....

UNIT 6 Manners

1 Jason is reading his mother's instructions. Choose the correct alternatives to complete her commands.

a .... late on weekdays.
○ Don't sleep   ○ Sleep

b .... for your exams.
○ Don't study   ○ Study

c .... with your brother.
○ Don't fight   ○ Fight

d .... your homework every day.
○ Don't do   ○ Do

e .... your sister with the housework.
○ Don't help   ○ Help

f .... too much time on the Internet.
○ Don't spend   ○ Spend

2 Match the photos to the orders or requests.

a

b

c

d

e

f

○ Don't eat too much chocolate.

○ Always wait for the green lights to cross the street.

○ Wear your seat belt.

○ Sit down, please.

○ Wash your hands before meals.

○ Don't litter.

3 Find the verbs in the word search to complete the school commands below.

A	G	J	L	Y	A	X	V	B	T	S	R	W	P	L	Z
U	S	E	Q	K	O	Y	W	K	H	O	F	E	D	V	C
Z	S	T	J	P	D	N	V	M	H	L	T	A	L	K	A
E	W	S	I	A	R	R	I	V	E	V	Y	R	E	S	W
R	A	I	S	E	S	O	R	C	X	E	B	H	J	Y	Q

a Don't .... your cell phone in the classroom.

b Always .... your uniform.

c .... at school punctually.

d Don't .... to your friends during explanations.

e .... your hand when you want to ask a question.

f .... your doubts with your teacher.

4 Read the text and circle the imperatives.

What can I do now to keep myself healthy and safe?

☑ Don't use any type of tobacco product.
Don't breathe secondhand cigarette smoke.

☑ Get regular exercise.

☑ Eat a healthy diet.

☑ Use your seat belt.

☑ Don't drink and drive.

☑ Wear protective headgear, such as motorcycle or bike helmets, when participating in sports.

☑ Don't swim alone.

☑ Talk to your parents or your doctor if you're feeling really sad.

☑ See your doctor regularly.

Adapted from <http://familydoctor.org>. Accessed on February 20, 2013.

5 Use the imperative forms of the verbs in the box to build the rules for behavior on the Internet.

> be (negative) • copy (negative) • finish • follow
> return • send on (negative) • start • try

Netiquette: Rules of Behavior on the Internet

- Always .... your messages with a greeting and .... them with your name.
- .... ironic. People who don't know who you really are may think you're mocking them.
- .... personal messages without acknowledging the source. Respect other people's privacy.
- .... emails immediately.
- .... all your friends on every email you send.
- .... standard language patterns.
- .... to use proper emotion icons (or emoticons) and acronyms (e.g., ASAP for "as soon as possible").

6 Which commands are used in the following situations? Unscramble the words to form sentences.

a The lights are on in your bedroom and you want to sleep.

You: .... (off / lights / the / turn)

b Someone's knocking at the door.

You: .... (in / please / come)

c Alice always tells lies.

Alice's mom: .... (lies / tell / don't / honey)

d A student wants to ask a question during the teacher's explanation.

Teacher: .... (hand / first / your / raise)

e Your friends are talking and laughing in the hospital corridor.

The nurse: ....!

(respect / be / some / quiet / show / and)

UNIT 7 Hello?

1 Complete the table with the *–ing* form of the verbs in the box, according to the examples.

> buy • carry • cook • enjoy • get • come
> listen • run • swim • take • watch • write

singing	riding	putting	flying

2 Fill in the blanks with the verbs in parentheses. Use the Present Continuous tense.

a Carl and John .... with their cousins. (play – affirmative)

b Tim .... lunch with his parents. (have – negative)

c .... Joana .... her bedroom? (paint – interrogative)

d He .... a bath. (take – negative)

e I .... at my beautiful clothes. (look – affirmative)

f .... you .... a text message? (send – interrogative)

3 Match the questions to the answers.

a Are they having lunch?

b Is she losing the game?

c Is he planning his holiday?

d Are you wearing your uniform?

e Is she washing the dishes?

f Am I interrupting?

○ No, she isn't. She is doing the laundry today.

○ Yes, she is. She isn't good at playing cards.

○ No, I'm not. Can't you see these are my regular clothes?

○ Yes, he is. He wants to visit Madrid.

○ No, you aren't. Come on in!

○ No, they aren't. They're cooking lunch.

21

4 Complete the sentences with the Present Continuous form of the verbs in the box. Then match the sentences to the photos.

> buy • drive • look for • rain • travel • use

a Paulo .... a new pair of shoes.

b Marisa .... to New York tonight.

c Marcel .... a public telephone now.

d .... Carlos and Mara .... a new cell phone?

e Amanda .... to work at this moment.

f .... it .... outside?

5 Change the sentences to the negative form.

a The boy is making a long distance call.

....

b You are waiting for the dial tone.

....

c She is searching for the correct city code.

....

d He is picking up the receiver to make a phone call.

....

e My husband and I are recording a message on our answering machine.

....

f They are listening to their voice messages.

....

6 Look at the photos and answer the questions. Use short answers.

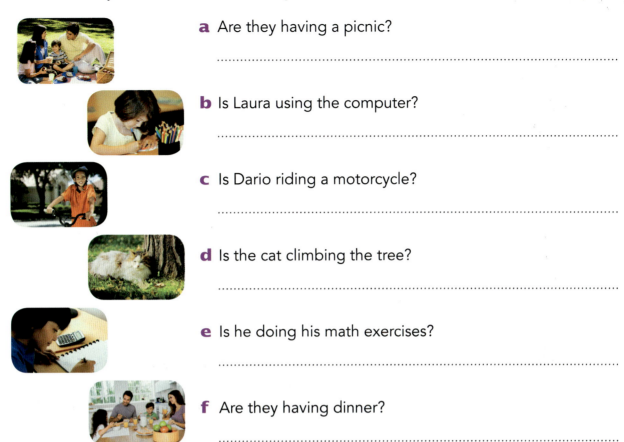

a Are they having a picnic?
....

b Is Laura using the computer?
....

c Is Dario riding a motorcycle?
....

d Is the cat climbing the tree?
....

e Is he doing his math exercises?
....

f Are they having dinner?
....

7 What are they doing? Write sentences about what these teens are doing during breaktime.

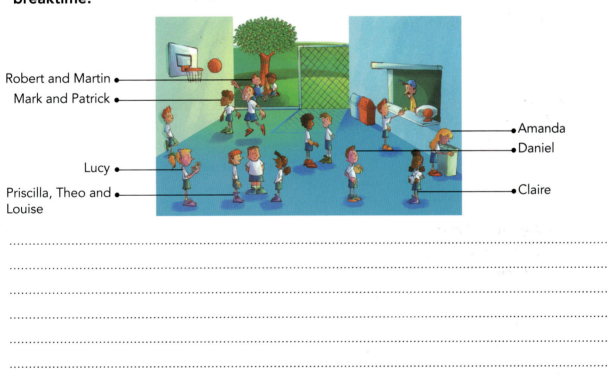

....
....
....
....
....
....

UNIT 8 — Art is everywhere

1 **What kind of art are these famous Brazilian artists related to?**

a Oscar Niemeyer designed many important buildings in Brazil such as the Contemporary Art Museum in Niteroi, the National Congress and the cathedral in Brasília.

Based on <http://www.biography.com>. Accessed on April 5, 2013.

....

b Candido Portinari's works can be found in galleries and museums in Brazil and abroad. His panels *Guerra e Paz* (War and Peace) are in the United Nations building in New York.

Based on <http://www.suapesquisa.com/biografias>. Accessed on April 5, 2013.

....

c Mario Quintana was born in Rio Grande do Sul. His poems are full of romance and humor. He is a very famous Brazilian writer.

Based on <http://www.releituras.com/mquintana_bio.asp>. Accessed on April 5, 2013.

....

d Sebastião Salgado is from Minas Gerais. He is considered one of the most important photographers of the early 21st century. He has been awarded numerous major prizes.

Based on <http://www.unicef.org/salgado/bio.htm>. Accessed on April 5, 2013.

....

e Ana Botafogo is the first ballerina of the Municipal Theater in Rio de Janeiro. She has danced in many different countries, representing Brazil.

Based on <http://www.anabotafogo.com.br/>. Accessed on April 5, 2013.

....

f Fernanda Montenegro is one of the best actresses in Brazil. She has performed in soap operas, films, and plays. Her husband was an actor and her daughter is also an actress.

Based on <http://educacao.uol.com.br/biografias>. Accessed on April 5, 2013.

....

2 Circle the correct words in the questions about graffiti artists and their art.

a A: **What / Where** do graffiti artists like to paint?

B: They frequently like to paint scenes or pictures with their own characters.

b A: **When / Where** do they do graffiti?

B: Only on walls they're allowed to draw on.

c A: **How / Who** do graffiti artists get their inspirations?

B: Each artist gets his/her inspiration in a different way.

d A: **When / What** do graffiti artists prefer to work?

B: A graffiti artist often prefers the night shift.

e A: **Who / What** are some famous graffiti artists you know?

B: They're Taki 183, Zephyr, Dondi, Phase 2, and Cope 2.

f A: **When / Where** do graffiti artists draw first: in their sketchbooks or on the walls?

B: They draw in their sketchbooks first.

3 Choose the correct questions for the answers below.

a ◯ Are you joining our dance competition?

◯ Who are you dancing with?

We're dancing with class 702.

b ◯ Does he play any musical instruments?

◯ What instrument does he play?

He plays the guitar.

c ◯ Is Katherine watching a movie?

◯ What time is Katherine watching a movie?

Yes, she's watching a great movie on TV.

d ◯ Do they have lunch at home?

◯ Where do they have lunch?

They have lunch at home.

4 Find out what's missing to complete the dialogs.

a **A:** .... are the boys sleeping?
B: They are sleeping in the living room.

b **A:** .... is Elton painting?
B: He's painting his house.

c **A:** .... does she practice ballet?
B: In the afternoon.

d **A:** .... do you call every morning?
B: My mom.

5 Unscramble the questions. Then choose the appropriate answers in the box to match them.

> In the cafeteria. • No, I'm not. I'm an only child. • No, they always arrive late.
> No, you aren't participating in this competition. • Only on weekdays.

a time / do / on / get / they / here / ?

....

b when / dog / Tina / does / the / walk / ?

....

c meet / where / your / do / friends / you / school ?

....

d sister / Susan's / you / are / ?

....

e team / am / tap dancing / I / your / on ?

....

6 Match the questions to the answers.

a Do you want to live abroad?   ◯ No, there isn't.

b What can she cook for lunch?   ◯ Sure, in London!

c Are the secretaries on vacation?   ◯ I don't think so. Maybe they're just a little late.

d Is there any milk in the fridge?   ◯ Next Friday evening, OK?

e When can we meet again?   ◯ Well, I don't think so. I prefer other kinds of art.

f Is graffiti cool?   ◯ Fried chicken.

Extra Reading 1

1 Read the text and complete the chart accordingly.

My schedule

Hi! I'm Andrea and this is my school schedule for the 7th grade. On Mondays I have history, drama, science, writing, and music. On Tuesdays I have math, geography, English, history, and French classes. I have P.E., social science, geography, writing, and English on Wednesdays. On Thursdays I have English, French, math, technology, and social science classes. And finally, on Fridays I have English, math, science, P.E., and technology. That's a pretty tough schedule, isn't it?

Monday	Tuesday	Wednesday	Thursday	Friday
history	math	P.E.	English	English
drama	geography			
science			math	science
	history	writing		
music	French	English	social science	technology

2 Match the columns to find answers to the questions about Andrea's schedule.

a Does Andrea have P.E. classes on Fridays?

b When does Andrea study technology?

c Does Andrea have writing classes on Tuesdays?

d How often does Andrea have English classes?

e How many classes does Andrea take every day?

◯ No, she doesn't.

◯ Yes, she does.

◯ She takes five different classes every day.

◯ On Thursdays and Fridays.

◯ Four times a week.

3 Write true (T) or false (F).

a Andrea doesn't have physical education classes. ◯

b Science classes are on Mondays and Fridays. ◯

c In Andrea's schedule there are no Spanish classes. ◯

d Andrea has math classes every weekday. ◯

e Andrea doesn't take French lessons on Thursdays. ◯

Extra Reading 2

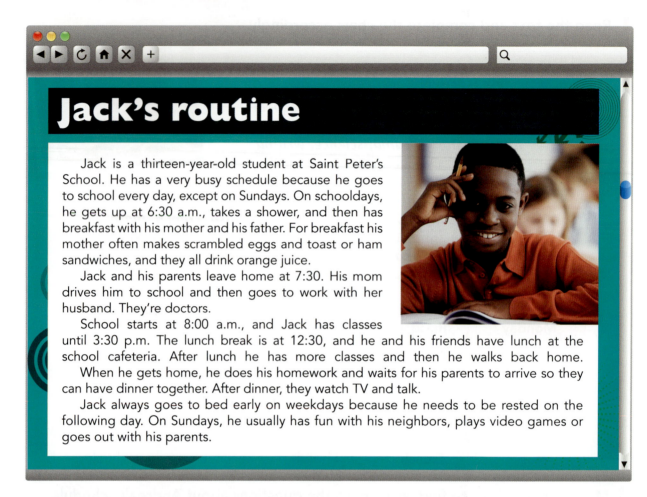

Jack's routine

Jack is a thirteen-year-old student at Saint Peter's School. He has a very busy schedule because he goes to school every day, except on Sundays. On schooldays, he gets up at 6:30 a.m., takes a shower, and then has breakfast with his mother and his father. For breakfast his mother often makes scrambled eggs and toast or ham sandwiches, and they all drink orange juice.

Jack and his parents leave home at 7:30. His mom drives him to school and then goes to work with her husband. They're doctors.

School starts at 8:00 a.m., and Jack has classes until 3:30 p.m. The lunch break is at 12:30, and he and his friends have lunch at the school cafeteria. After lunch he has more classes and then he walks back home.

When he gets home, he does his homework and waits for his parents to arrive so they can have dinner together. After dinner, they watch TV and talk.

Jack always goes to bed early on weekdays because he needs to be rested on the following day. On Sundays, he usually has fun with his neighbors, plays video games or goes out with his parents.

1 Complete the statements about the text.

a Jack studies at ....

b He has breakfast with his .... and ...., and they often have scrambled .... and .... or ham ....

c Jack goes to school by .... His .... drives him there.

d Jack has classes before and after ....

e Jack doesn't go to sleep .... on weekdays; on the contrary, he goes to bed early.

2 Answer the questions according to the text.

a How old is Jack?

....

b What is Jack's parents' profession?

....

28

Extra Reading 3

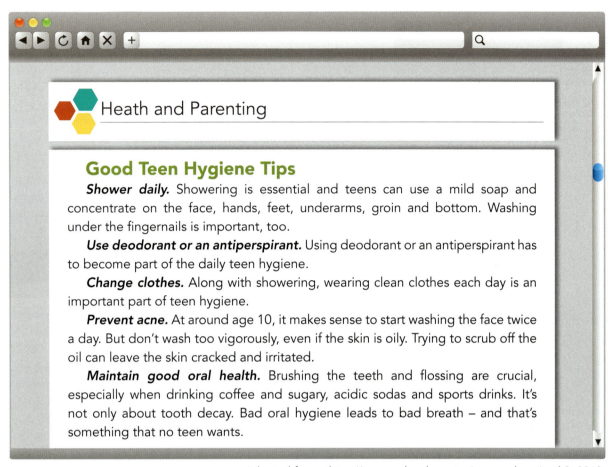

Heath and Parenting

Good Teen Hygiene Tips

Shower daily. Showering is essential and teens can use a mild soap and concentrate on the face, hands, feet, underarms, groin and bottom. Washing under the fingernails is important, too.

Use deodorant or an antiperspirant. Using deodorant or an antiperspirant has to become part of the daily teen hygiene.

Change clothes. Along with showering, wearing clean clothes each day is an important part of teen hygiene.

Prevent acne. At around age 10, it makes sense to start washing the face twice a day. But don't wash too vigorously, even if the skin is oily. Trying to scrub off the oil can leave the skin cracked and irritated.

Maintain good oral health. Brushing the teeth and flossing are crucial, especially when drinking coffee and sugary, acidic sodas and sports drinks. It's not only about tooth decay. Bad oral hygiene leads to bad breath – and that's something that no teen wants.

Adapted from <http://www.webmd.com>. Accessed on April 9, 2013.

1 Read each statement below and check the correct column.

Statements	Yes	No
a I wash my face twice a day.		
b I brush my teeth after I drink coffee.		
c I take at least one shower a day.		
d I use antiperspirant.		
e I wear clean clothes every day.		

2 Which tip was **NOT** mentioned in the text?

a Don't scrub off the oil on your face. ○

b Clean your nails. ○

c Don't wear dirty clothes. ○

d Don't pick your nose. ○

e Use a mild soap in your shower. ○

29

Extra Reading 4

Healthy Breakfast Ideas

Morning meals that help you lose weight, do better in sports, and not feel hungry.

By **Molly Raisch**

The Most Important Meal of the Day

No doubt about it, breakfast is the most important meal of the day — it activates your brain and keeps you slim. In fact, studies show that people who skip breakfast tend to be heavier than people who eat a healthy breakfast. When you're too busy or just not hungry, there are delicious alternatives to your breakfast. One of these is the right solution to match your lifestyle, health, and weight loss objectives.

1. If you don't have time to eat a complete breakfast, try Greek yogurt; it is a powerful breakfast substitution.
2. If you need something fast, have a piece of fruit or a nut bar.
3. If the drive-thru is your only option, avoid muffins, bagels, and pancakes, and order a protein-packed egg sandwich instead.
4. If you're never hungry 'til noon, drink a milk shake to start your day with vitamins and nutrients.

5. If you need to intensify your exercising, carbs and protein are essential for repairing your muscles post sweat session.
6. If you're trying to lose 10 kilos, try a mug of green tea to accelerate your metabolism.
7. If heart health is your priority, try a breakfast burrito filled with foods high in monounsaturated fats such as avocados, peanut butter, and many nuts and seeds, as well as olive oil, canola oil, etc.
8. If you need more fiber, have a cereal portion with more than 5 g of fiber.

Adapted from <http://www.prevention.com>. Accessed on April 8, 2013.

1 Check the correct statements according to the article.

- **a** The text explains that people who don't have breakfast are healthy and tend to be thin. ○
- **b** Greek yogurt is a good suggestion when you can't have a real meal in the morning. ○
- **c** The article says that a piece of fruit or a nut bar is the perfect breakfast for everybody. ○
- **d** Green tea is good for people who are trying to lose weight. ○
- **e** If you are worried about your heart, you can have the famous Mexican burrito stuffed with healthy ingredients. ○

Extra Reading 5

How to Use a Public Phone
By **Racheal Ambrose, eHow Contributor**

Cell phones are all around us, but people still use public phones. To use them, we need to have a predetermined amount of money to make a phone call. The rates vary depending on the location. Consumers make both local and long-distance calls on public phones. According to *USA Today*, public phones are not in good conditions and they are not very accessible because people don't use them very much.

Instructions
1 Pick up the phone from the receiver.
2 Insert the proper amount of change using nickels, dimes and quarters. Dial a calling card number if you are using one.
3 Dial "1" plus the area code and phone number.
4 Wait for the person you are calling to answer. Talk. If the person or the voicemail does not answer your call, you get your money back.
5 Add more coins when the phone asks you to.
6 Hang up the phone when the call is over.

Tips & Warnings
Dial 0 to talk to an operator.
Dial 911 in an emergency.

Adapted from <http://www.ehow.com>. Accessed on April 9, 2013.

1 Read the text and choose the best words in *italics* to complete the sentences.

　a Nowadays, there aren't many public phones because some aren't functioning well and because people don't *dial / use* them so much anymore.

　b On public phones we *can / can't* make local and long-distance calls.

　c To make a call, public phones charge a predetermined rate which varies according to the *consumer / location*.

　d When using a public phone, if the person you're calling does not *dial / answer*, you get your money back.

　e If you want to talk to an *emergency / operator*, dial 0.

2 Number the sentences below according to the sequence of instructions in the text.

　◯ When the call is answered, you can talk as long as you wish, but remember to add more coins.
　◯ Pick up the receiver.
　◯ Dial the number you want to contact and wait until someone answers your call.
　◯ After finishing the call, hang up the receiver.
　◯ Insert the coins.

31

Extra Reading 6

PROPER DENTAL HYGIENE

Visit the dentist.

Bleed profusely.

Out of shame, start flossing.

Give up after two days.

Schedule an appointment 6-12 months later.

Floss the night before.

Repeat.

1 Which statements are correct, according to the strip above?

   a After visiting the dentist, the boy decides to start flossing.

   b The boy starts flossing because he is embarrassed.

   c The boy stops flossing every day after 6-12 months.

   d The boy has another appointment with the dentist two days after his first visit.

   e The dental hygiene habit described in the strip is not correct.

2 Read these comments about some people's dental hygiene and write GH for good habits and BH for bad habits.

   a Helen brushes her teeth after meals.

   b My brother doesn't floss every day.

   c I don't have snacks between meals often, but when I do, I always brush afterwards.

   d Daniel and Gloria visit the dentist once every five years.

   e I only floss on the day before I visit the dentist.